Write from the Start 4

Lynn Michell

Oliver & Boyd

Illustrated by: Barry Wilkinson, Trevor Parkin, Pat Tourret, Linda Birch, Jo Worth, Frances Livens, Mick Davis, Rowan Barnes Murphy, David Simmonds, Bob Geary, Michael Charlton, Lesley Smith, Joanna Williams, Stephen Gibson.
Cover illustration by Barry Wilkinson

Oliver & Boyd
Robert Stevenson House
1–3 Baxter's Place
Leith Walk
Edinburgh EH1 3BB

A Division of Longman Group UK Ltd

First published 1987

ISBN 0 05 003947 4

Set in 14 on 16pt Helvetica
Produced by Longman Group (FE) Ltd.
Printed in Hong Kong

Contents

Teacher's Note

Write from the Start is a series of six books for children between the ages of six and twelve. It is designed to encourage children's awareness of the different purposes of writing and to develop their ability to use and apply its different forms for a variety of audiences.

The series covers both the expressive and the functional aspects of writing: stories; word play leading to poetry; speech bubbles leading to writing plays; messages of various kinds; instructions and information both given and received.

Book 2 develops and extends the work of the introductory level (Book 1) and invites the child to go beyond the activities given on the page. In Books 3 and 4 the framework and starting points for the writing tasks remain but there is more scope for children to draw on their own ideas and experiences as they write for different purposes and audiences. In Books 5 and 6 these props are gradually withdrawn and the varied writing tasks make considerable demands on children's abilities to think, plan and write appropriate texts.

It is not recommended that children be left to work through the books in isolation. There are ample opportunities for discussion and role-play (especially in the 'Voices' units) and teachers should feel free to extend and adapt all of the suggestions offered here. Indeed, without discussion and teacher participation, the effectiveness of this material will be reduced.

Teachers should also be selective and adaptable in the order in which they use the various units. We have offered an arrangement which makes logical sense and represents a progression within each unit. You may well have different ideas, though, and you should use these materials as a flexible resource rather than a strait-jacket. Take what you want at the time that suits you best. The important thing is to cover all these varieties of writing at some time during the school year.

The series does not set out to teach all aspects of English; it concerns itself with developing children's concepts of themselves as writers, their awareness of different writing styles and the various purposes to which writing skills need to be applied.

1 Voices

What are they saying?

Here's A.P.P. — Another Planet Person.
He is visiting earth.
He wants to know more about the way we talk,
and what we talk about.
He spends a lot of time listening to our conversations.

You can help A.P.P.
Imagine what the children below are saying.
The pictures will give you some clues.
Write a short conversation for **one** of the pictures.

Conversations

A.P.P. is getting better at guessing what people
are talking about, even when he cannot hear the words.
He knows that certain things will give him clues:
- the place where the conversation takes place
- the people themselves
- the look on their faces.

For instance, A.P.P. can guess that the two earth people
in this picture have just spotted an alien space-craft.

Sometimes A.P.P. cannot guess what earth people are saying.
You can help him.
Here are two more scenes.
Can you guess what the people are saying in each?

Choose **one** of the pictures above (including the spaceship).
Imagine the conversation between the people in the picture.
Try it out with a friend.
Write a short conversation to fit the scene.

Now **try** a second picture.

A.P.P. says

I know that the way we say something depends on who we are talking to. Like this:

Look at the pictures below.
In each pair the same person is saying more or less the same thing,
but in two quite different ways.
Decide what the person is saying in each picture.
Write the words spoken and draw speech bubbles round them.

1

2

Saying a lot

Sometimes on the telephone we need to give a lot of information
to another person.
We do most of the talking.
The other person mostly listens.
Like this:

RECEPTIONIST	Hello . . . Dental Surgery.
NICOLA	Hello . . . my name is Nicola Garrod. I'm afraid I will have to cancel a dental appointment with Mr Ross.
RECEPTIONIST	Yes . . . when was it for?
NICOLA	For next Tuesday at 4.30 . . . can I make another . . . ? (and so on)

Below are three more ideas for telephone conversations
in which **you** do most of the talking.
Choose **one**.
Act it out with a friend.
Write a short telephone conversation like the one above.

1. **Call** a phone number given on a card in a pet shop window
   which asks for good homes for kittens.

2. **Call** the big toy shop in town and ask if they stock something
   you particularly want for your next birthday.

3. **Call** your local Chinese, Indian or Fish and Chip shop
   and order a Take-away meal for your family.

Saying a little

Sometimes on the telephone we need to say very little.
We know the other person.
The other person is expecting our phone call.

What do you think these two boys are talking about?

FARAI   Hi . . . is that Mel?

MELVYN   Yeh . . . Hi.

FARAI   Can you come?

MELVYN   Yeh.

FARAI   Great . . . when?

MELVYN   About half an hour?

FARAI   Fine . . . see you.

MELVYN   See you . . . Bye.

FARAI   Bye.

Here are two more ideas for conversations
in which both people need to say very little.
Choose **one**. Or make up a different conversation of your own.
Act out the whole conversation before you write it down.
Then **write** your conversation as we have done.

1. Ring your mum to tell her briefly that you are staying
   to have tea at your Gran's.

2. Ring your best friend and tell him or her that you've found
   a great place for your secret gang meetings. (Remember it's a
   secret. Don't give too much away to anyone who might be
   listening.)

Fairy tale conversations

In cartoon pictures the words people speak are in speech bubbles.
Like this:

Sometimes in stories there are no pictures with speech bubbles.
Instead there are **speech marks** for the words characters speak.
Everything inside a speech bubble can be written inside speech marks.
Like this:

''Who's that trip-trapping over
my bridge?'' yelled the Troll.

''It's me. The biggest Billy Goat
Gruff!'' shouted the goat.

Now **do the same** for Little Red Riding Hood.
We have started it for you.

Look at the other pictures on this page.

Write each conversation for a story without pictures.
Remember to say who is speaking each time.

Characters in search of a story

Here are some characters in search of a story.
I hope you have an idea for one of them.

Choose **one** character.
Think of a story about this character.
Now choose just one scene from your story.
Show the scene from the story in a cartoon picture.
Use speech bubbles to show what the characters are saying.
Then **write** the same conversation for a story without pictures.

Cartoon conversations

Here is a cartoon.
The story is told in pictures and speech bubbles.

Write the whole story in your own words but without pictures
or speech bubbles. Say what is happening in each picture,
including the ones with no speech bubbles.

Remember to include what the characters say in speech marks,
and to say who is speaking.

2 Word Play

Tasty

Here's A.P.P. again.
He wants to know more about the things we eat.
He wants to try some of our food himself.
What should he choose?

You help A.P.P. decide what things to eat.
Tell him about your favourite food.
Try to describe the exact taste and texture.
We have started a list for you.
Write several more things that you love to eat.
Draw a picture for each one, like we have done.

	JELLY tastes fruity, slippery, liquid,
	CRISPS taste salty,...
	LEMONADE tastes....

14

You must also tell A.P.P. about food and drink which you really don't like.

Warn him **not** to try some things!

You can make your message stronger by writing a word picture.
One way to do this is to say that the food is **like** something else.
Look at the examples below.

SEMOLINA is like slimy frogspawn.

MELON tastes like soap.

My TUMMY MEDICINE is just like camel's spit.

Tell A.P.P. what your worst foods are like.
If you want you can draw pictures, too, as we have done.
Write about three or four horrible things to eat or drink.

Come and Buy!

Imagine you've just opened your own market stall.
You want everyone to buy **your** food.
What would you write on your notices to tempt people?

Draw your own stall with you behind it.
You will need lots of room on the page.
Decide what you want to sell (anything you can eat).
Draw in your food.
Write notices which accurately describe what you are selling
and tempt people to buy.

Look at the pictures on this page.
Think of words that describe the sounds in each picture.

We have done the first one for you.

— roar
— crackle
— hiss
— snap

Write two or three sound-words for each picture.
Choose the best words you can think of.

Imagine you are in one of the places shown in the pictures.
You choose which one.
Imagine the sounds and noises in the place you have chosen.
Write what you can hear.
We have begun the first one for you.

I can hear:
the howling wind,
the hiss of surf on shingle,
the waves crashing against
    the rocks,
the clink-clink-clink of
    the ropes against the
    masts,
the shrill cries of the
    circling gulls.

I can hear:
the loud speakers,

What else?

I can hear:

I can hear:

Use your list of sounds to help you write a paragraph
about **one** of the pictures.
Don't just write out your list.
Write sentences describing the sounds and noises.
Make your paragraph detailed and interesting to read.
Make a sound picture with words.

Smelly

Some places have very definite smells, don't they?
A particular smell can remind you strongly
of a particular place.
A smell can conjure up memories and feelings.

Below are two places with very particular smells.
Look at each picture in turn and imagine the smells in the place.
Write a list of the smells you imagine.

I can smell:

I can smell:

Choose **one** of the places above.
Use your list of smells to help you **write** a paragraph
about one of the pictures.

Now **write** another paragraph about a different place.
You choose where.

House of Horrors

Imagine you are in the House of Horrors at the fair.
It is very dark and you can see very little.
But you can feel things!
Lots of horrible, scary things that send tingles down your spine.
Imagine your hands reaching out and touching.
Imagine objects sliding and scraping against your face.
What do you feel?

Look carefully at the picture and
write about some of the things
you can see, or imagine
a different House of Horrors of your own.

We have begun a description of the House of Horrors.
You continue it.

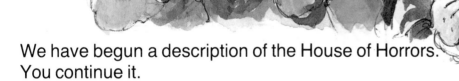

It is almost black-dark in the House of
Horrors. There is just a red glow here
and there at floor level. I can feel
icy drops of water on my face....

Connections

Look at the pair of pictures below.

A.P.P. is running as fast
as he can.

His bus is ready to leave
the bus stop.

We can think of a link between the pictures.
There are several ways we can show the link in our writing.

1. A.P.P. is running **because** he wants to catch the bus.
2. A.P.P. is running **so that** he won't miss the bus.
3. **If** A.P.P. doesn't hurry he will miss the bus.
4. A.P.P. ran fast **but** he still missed the bus.
5. **Although** A.P.P. ran as fast as he could he **still** missed the bus.

Look at the pairs of pictures on the next page.
Write a sentence to show how each pair of pictures is connected.
Remember to find better words than **and** or **then**.

Look at the connecting words on the next page.

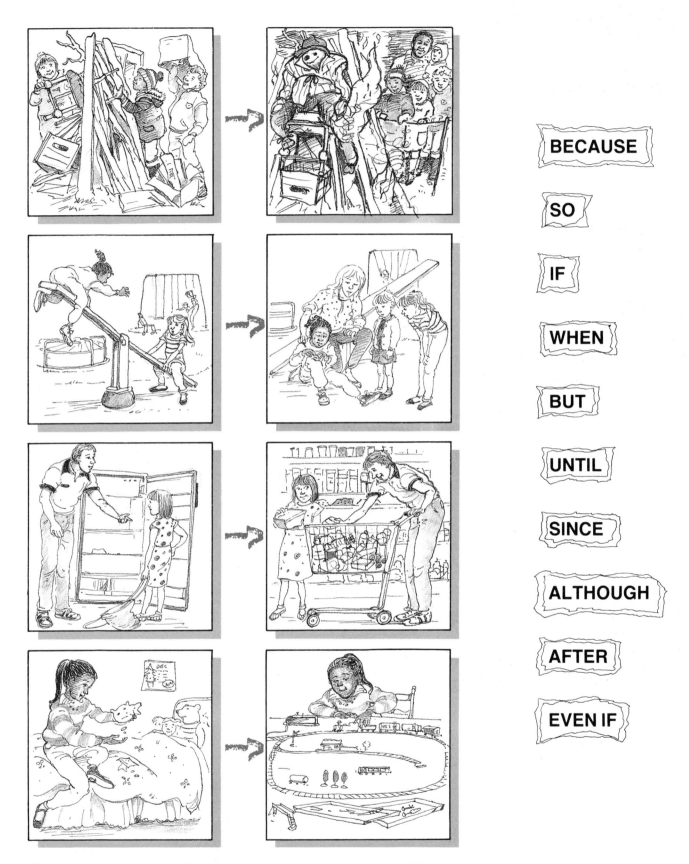

Draw two pictures of your own that are connected in some way.
Write something to show how they are linked.

The picture strip below tells a short story.
We have written a story for the picture strip
but we have missed out all the connecting words.
Look at the pictures and read the story.
Write out the story, adding your own connecting words.

_____there were only four weeks left before the next Judo grading,
Alex decided to try for his green belt. _____he passed, he would
be in the same class as his friend Michael. Each week he listened
carefully to his instructor _____ he would miss nothing. At home he
learnt the names of the movements _____ practised the exercises.
_____ it was the day of the grading. Alex got top marks. His
instructor said he deserved his special certificate _____ he had
worked so hard.

Write a short story for one of the picture strips below.
The last part of the story especially needs explaining.
Choose your connecting words carefully to explain
the last link in the story.

Ian gets a fright

Clue: Why is the boy so relieved?

The legend of Icarus

Clue: Why are Icarus's wings melting?

Make up a story of your own in the same way.

Fairy tale characters

In fairy tales characters are often very simple.
We can imagine what they look like (if we are not given a picture).
We can guess how they will behave.

Princesses are beautiful,
innocent, kind, gentle.

Giants are greedy, ugly,
huge, selfish, cruel.

Queens are vain, proud,
jealous, beautiful, wicked.

Here is a typical description of a Princess:

The youngest princess was the loveliest of them all.
Even the sun marvelled at her beauty. Her eyes were
clear and blue like the pools in the palace gardens.
Her hair was as gold as honey. Often she would sit in
the shade of a weeping willow while the birds and
butterflies perched happily beside her.

Here are some more fairy tale characters.
Write four or five words to describe each one,
as we did on the opposite page.

Kings are . . . .

Witches are . . . .

Dwarves are . . . .

Woodcutters are . . . .

Step-mothers are . . . .

Choose **one** of the fairy tale characters you have described.
Write a paragraph for a story book describing your character.
You may like to use ideas from fairy tales you can remember.
Begin your description:

Once upon a time there lived a...

Fairy tale animals

Animals in fairy tales often behave like humans.
They talk and think like humans.
But they are usually very simple characters,
like princesses and witches.
We can guess what they are going to do.

Here are some fairy tale animals.
Write three or four words to describe two of the animals,
as you did before.

Cats are . . . .

Deer fawns are . . . .

Foxes are . . . .

Choose **one** of the fairy tale animals.
Write a short paragraph for a story book describing your animal.
You may like to use ideas from stories you can remember.
Begin your description:

Once long ago there lived a...

Fairy tales for younger children

You can be a real author.
You can write a fairy tale to be read aloud to younger children.
Here are some things to think about and do before you start writing.

Before writing
Decide which class you want to write for.
A nursery or infant class would be best.
Visit the class, if you can, and talk to the children and their teacher about their favourite story books.
Look at some of the story books on the shelves.
Look at the way they are written with short sentences and simple words.

Planning your story
Now you know more about the kind of story young children like.
Plan your story in rough.
Use one of the ideas on the next page or make up a different story of your own.
Remember to plan your story with a beginning, middle and end.

Ideas for fairy tales

1. Here are some characters looking for a story!
   Make up a short story for one of them.

OR 2. Make up a short story about one of the following:
   a good witch   *an ugly princess*   *a kind giant*
   a frog who is really a prince

OR 3. Make up a story about a child who goes on a magic journey
   to a fairy tale land.

Writing drafts

Write a rough draft of your story.
Remember to write simply and clearly.
Show the draft to your teacher.
What changes are needed to make your story even better?
You may need to write two or three drafts until you are satisfied with
your story.
This is the way adult authors work.

Final draft

Plan the layout of your story, including spaces for pictures.
Write your story and colour the pictures.
Design a bright, attractive cover for your story.

Now your story is ready to be read to the younger children.

4 Messages

Away from home

Imagine you are going to stay with a friend for a week.
Here are a few of the things you will need to take.

| pyjamas | toothbrush | anorak | money | warm jumper |

But aren't there lots of other important things?
What else would you want to take?

Write in rough a list of things you would want to take
to your friend's.
Then use headings like the ones below to help you
organise your list.

| Clothes | Wash-things | Toys and Games |

Write your final list neatly using your own headings.

Please remember

Before you go to stay with your friend you need to write
a list of reminders for someone else in your family.
They must remember to do all the things you usually do.

What needs to be done while **you** are away?
Write your own reminder note for someone in your family.

Please Remember

1. Write note for one of my friends
   to take to swimming club.
2. Water my plant.
3. Feed fish. One pinch of food every
   day.
4. Collect Mrs. Hardy's paper from
   newsagent each evening.

Diary

You enjoyed your week with your friend very much.
There were special treats and interesting outings.
Now you are home again.
You want to write up your diary so that you will remember
some of the things that happened.

Write a Diary entry for the best day.
Write about the things that were important to you.
You can write notes rather than long sentences.
Like this:

> Saturday May 7th
>
> 8.45. Breakfast with all the family.
> Bacon rolls, toast, butter and
> strawberry jam, hot chocolate!

Remember a diary is personal.
It is for **you** to read at a later date.
You choose what to write and how you write it.

Dear A.P.P. . . .

Pretend you are in hospital for a week.
A.P.P. will come and visit you while you are there.
You're fairly sure he will bring you something!
What would you like?

Your mum says you can write a letter and she will deliver it.
Perhaps you could hint politely that there is something
you would like!

Write a letter to A.P.P.
Remember to tell him:

- the name of the hospital
- what you are in for
- how long you expect to be there
- visiting hours
- what you would like!

Can you remember how to lay out a letter?
If not, look back at page 41 of Book 3.

Thank you for . . .

The hospital post has just arrived.
The children in your class have sent you lots of cards.
Your teacher has sent a big book of games and puzzles.
You are really pleased!

Write a cheerful thank you letter to all your class.
Remember it will be read out aloud by your teacher.
Tell everyone one or two things about your stay in hospital.
Choose things that you think will interest them.
Tell them when you hope to be back at school.
Draw and write an envelope to go with the letter.

Write a second letter to your very best friend.
In this letter you can include all the things you didn't put
in the other one.
You can describe all the gory details.
You can make it all sound dreadful if you want.
Draw and write an envelope to go with this second letter.

Watching TV

Square eyes

Your mum says you watch too much television.
You watch *anything* that comes on.

She says she will limit you to two programmes an evening.
They must finish before 8 pm.
On Saturdays you can watch two hours television during the day.
You can also watch two hours in the evening before 9 pm.

Make a list of your favourite programmes —
the ones you really couldn't bear to miss.
(Invent names for programmes if you like.)
Write a timetable for the week.
Give the name and time of each programme.
We have begun a timetable to show you how.

MON.	4.40 Dungeons and Dragons 5.00 Blue Peter	20 mins. 30 mins.
TUE.	5.10 Star Trek 7.00 Pop Quiz	50 mins. 30 mins.
WED.		

Star letter

Some children write to the TV companies to say
how much they have enjoyed a particular programme.
Some children write in to complain.
Each week the writer of the most interesting letter is invited
to the TV Studios in London.
The writer reads the letter personally on the programme.

Write a letter about a programme
you have seen recently.
If you enjoyed the programme and
want more —
Or if you hated the programme —
you must say **why**.

Perhaps your teacher will send one or two of the best letters
from your class to the TV company.

A.P.P. wrote a letter to the TV company.
This is part of a letter he received in reply.

```
Please come to Television House in London on
Tuesday 3rd May by 1.00pm.  Your mother or
father can come with you.  We will have lunch
together and then go into the TV studios to
record you reading your letter.

We do hope you can come and look forward to
meeting you very much.
```

Imagine that **your** letter has been chosen as Letter-of-the-Week!
You are invited to the Studio.
What do you reply?
Write a letter saying you can or cannot come.

Nell is watching the TV news while her mum is getting tea
in the kitchen.
One item is of special interest to her family.
She runs to tell her mum.
Her message is short and includes a comment of her own.

1

Due to the continuing dispute about pay and conditions, there will be a 24-hour strike on the railways tomorrow. A representative from the train drivers' union said that no trains will run from midnight tonight....

2

Mum, there's going to be a train strike tomorrow. How will Granny get here?

Here are some more news items.
Imagine that they are of special interest to you
or someone in your family.
You run to tell someone else.
What do you say?
Write a brief message for each as we have done
in Picture 2 above.

And now something of interest for younger viewers. Next week all over Britain, Sport Centres are holding special talent-spotting sessions. They are looking for talented youngsters to be given free training over the next three years in swimming, football and athletics....

Well, tonight is the big night for pop fans. The special all-night concert in aid of Food for Africa will be broadcast live from Hyde Park. The concert will begin at six tonight and throughout there will be appeals for donations.

Messages

Sometimes you have to think hard to pick out the message
you are receiving.
Yesterday, on her way to school,
Kim met her neighbour, Mrs Hardy.
Mrs Hardy is an old lady who always has a lot to say!
This is what she told Kim:

> Hello dear, isn't it a lovely day. I'm glad I bumped into you because I was on my way to see your mother, then I remembered I was out of coffee and so I went to the corner shop. I know coffee's cheaper in the supermarket but there you are ... anyway I was going to ask your mother if I could possibly leave my front door key with her late this afternoon because I'm expecting the plumber ... what a mess that leak has made. You see I have to visit an old friend in hospital at five so when you get home from school could you warn your mum to expect me ....

> Yes, I'll tell her. I'm afraid I must go or I'll be late for school.

When Kim arrived home from school, her mum was out.
Kim had to go out too.
She left a note about Mrs Hardy on the kitchen table.
Write the message Kim left.

Remember: messages should be **brief** and **clear**.
They should include the important information — and no more.
They should not be like Mrs Hardy's conversation!

Think about the following situations.

Then **write** a suitable message for each.

1. It is 9 o'clock on a Tuesday morning. Your teacher decides to take your class to the hall for an extra rehearsal of the Christmas play. She asks you to leave a clear message on the blackboard for the two children who have not arrived in school yet.

   Write the message you leave on the blackboard.

2. Barry's gang is going to meet after school today to discuss suggestions for a Saturday outing. Now you can't meet the others because of a dentist appointment. You need to see them in the playground at break. You want to ask one of the others to put forward your suggestion for you.

   Write the message you pass round the others.

3. Think of another situation where **you** have to write a message for someone. Describe the situation as we have done.

   Then **write** the message.

5 Instructions

Symbols

Some notices give information and directions without words.
Pictures take the place of writing.
These pictures are called **symbols**.
Here are some you may know:

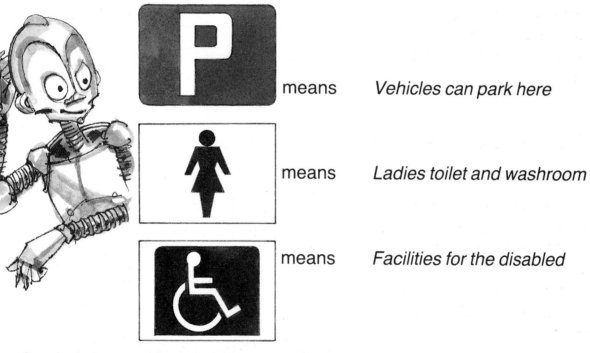

means   *Vehicles can park here*

means   *Ladies toilet and washroom*

means   *Facilities for the disabled*

Symbols have to fit the place where they are to be placed.
The place also helps us work out what the symbol means.
Symbols need to be eye-catching and simple.
They are useful for people who can't read
or don't know the language — like A.P.P.

Design symbols for **three** of the following.
Remember they need to be instantly understood.

Bus Stop	*Park*
Library	*Children's Playground*
School	*Café or Snack Bar*
Police	*Swimming Pool*

Think of something else that needs a symbol.
Design one.

Machine buttons

Many machines have buttons and controls that show symbols.
The symbols tell us what the controls are for,
like those on the cassette recorder below.
Can you work out what they all mean?

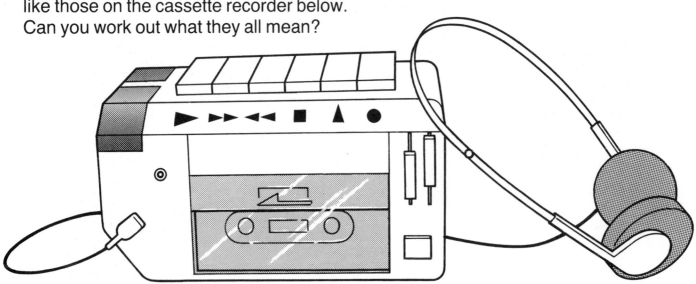

On the next page is a machine that's not been invented yet.
It has six different controls.

What does the machine do?
Play a video-game?
Give you crisps?
Run your favourite TV show?
You decide what the machine does.
Write what each control button is for.
Design a symbol for each button.
Like this:

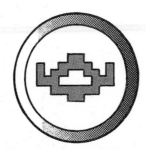

1. Push to play video-game

2. Press to deliver crisps

If this machine is not right for what **you** want it to do, you can design a different one of your own.

Space Invaders

You will have seen machines like this Space Invaders Game.
Here are the *Rules of the Game*.

1. Aliens are attacking your planet. Your mission is to destroy them.

2. You are the gun base at the bottom of the screen. You can **fire** at the aliens with your laser. You can move the gun base to the **left** and to the **right**.

3. The aliens can destroy you with their bombs. You only have three lives.

4. You can put up a protective **shield** for three seconds but you can only use it five times in each game.

Design symbols for the **four controls** so that children will know instantly what they are for.

Design a game of your own like Space Invaders.
1. Think about how the game will work.
2. Decide on the *Rules of the Game*.
3. **Draw** your screen with controls and symbols.
4. **Write** out the *Rules of the Game*, like we have done.

Your room

Jo's bedroom door looks like this!

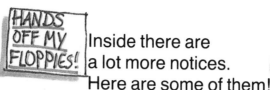

Inside there are a lot more notices. Here are some of them!

Make and decorate some instructions for your bedroom door and your room.
You can do lots or just a few.
Your notices should tell us a little bit about you.

Your classroom

Perhaps there are some instructions needed for your classroom.
Ask your teacher if there are any for you to make.

Tidying up

Inside Jo's room there are lots of fun notices.
There is also A TERRIBLE MESS!

Imagine that you are Jo.
You have to tidy your room.
(What a dreadful thought!)
Write a list of instructions to make the task easier.
Divide the task into smaller tasks and do one at a time.
We have begun the list for you.
You finish it.

Tidying My Room

1. Pick up all the clothes and put them in cupboards and drawers.

2. Find all the books...

45

How to get there

The map on this page shows part of a town.
Imagine that you live at 15 Park Crescent.
Soon some friends are coming to stay with your family.
They will arrive by train.
Write them a short letter.
Tell them how to walk from the station to your house.

It will help if you number your directions.
Like this:

1. Cross over Station Street using the zebra crossing.

2. Walk past the shops...

(You continue the directions.)

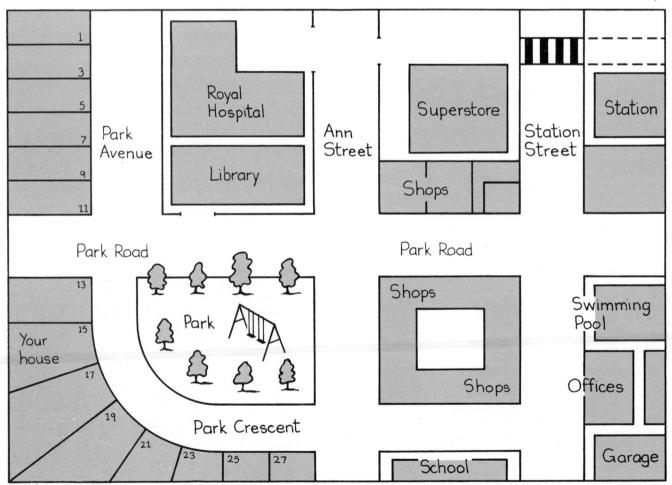

If you can't remember how to lay out a letter,
look back at page 41 in Book 3.

Your friends have arrived.
They are Mr and Mrs Elliot, Linda aged 10 and Kevin aged 9.
They are enjoying their stay with you.

Mr and Mrs Elliott want to go shopping
in the big new superstore in Ann Street.
They do not know their way around the town.
Write them some numbered directions explaining the way.
(Use the map on page 46 to help you.)

You and Kevin want to go swimming
but Linda wants to go to the library.
Her parents say she can go on her own.
Write some numbered directions for Linda.
Make them very simple and clear.
Try to tell her things to look out for on the way.

Here's A.P.P. again.
He's visiting your town.

You know how to do all sorts of things in town,
like making a phone call from a telephone box.
A.P.P. doesn't.
You need to explain things to him so that he can do them too.

Write simple, numbered instructions for A.P.P.
explaining how to make a phone call.
You choose whether you write instructions
for a telephone kiosk or a new, push-button callbox.
Order is very important.
Write a rough draft first and check that the order is correct.
We have begun some instructions for you:

1. Check that you have the right money.
2. Check that you have the number ready.
3. Lift the receiver and wait for the dialling tone.
4.

(You continue.)

Flow Diagrams

Another way to write instructions is to put each step in a separate box.
We can make a very simple *Flow Diagram*, like this.

> Check that you have the right money.

▼

> Check that you have the number ready.

▼

> Lift the receiver and wait for the dialling tone.

(and so on)

Write a simple Flow Diagram for A.P.P. for **two** of the following:

How to post a letter.

How to buy a bag of crisps from the corner shop.

How to borrow a library book.

Problem on the line

So far your instructions for A.P.P. have gone very smoothly.
But supposing he meets a problem.
For example, when A.P.P. picks up the receiver
in the phone box, he cannot hear the dialling tone.
You've not told him what to do about this.
You need to change your simple Flow Diagram.
You need to add a loop and **yes** and **no** boxes.

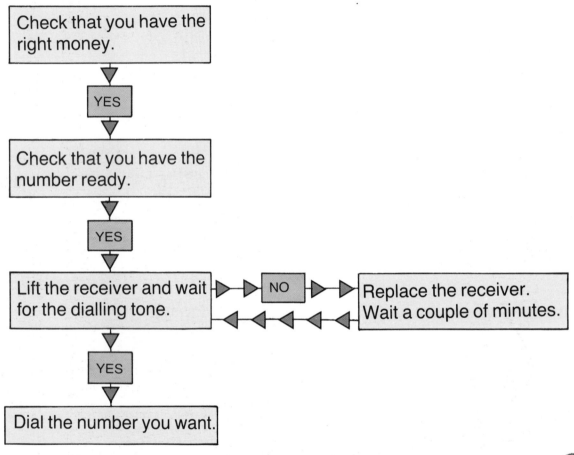

Check that you have the right money.

YES

Check that you have the number ready.

YES

Lift the receiver and wait for the dialling tone. → NO → Replace the receiver. Wait a couple of minutes.

YES

Dial the number you want.

(and so on)

Imagine A.P.P. meets a problem when he goes
to post a letter.
He has no stamp!
Write a new Flow Diagram like the one above.
Add a single loop telling A.P.P. what to do
if he has no stamp.
Add YES and NO boxes.

Dos and don'ts

Around the town there are all kinds of notices.
Some tell us what to do.
Some tell us what not to do.

A.P.P. visited a friend in hospital today.
On the ward door there were three notices:

WARD 3

Two visitors only to each bed please

NO SMOKING

VISITING TIMES
MON, TUES, THURS, FRI, 7-8PM
WED, SAT, SUN. 2-3PM, 7-8PM

Design and **write** some notices that give instructions
for two of these places.

1. The park
2. On the bus
3. The library
4. A petrol station
5. The swimming pool

Play Place

This is a miserable sort of a place, isn't it?
Just look at the notices!
Not many children would want to play here.

Imagine your own Play Place.
Think of somewhere where children would have lots of fun.
It could be a park or a garden or a fair.
It could be something quite different,
like a Fun Palace or a Space-Age Playground
where all the rides are free.

Design and **write** notices for your Play Place.
They should give information and instructions.
They should also be welcoming and fun!
If you like, draw a picture of your Play Place with the notices.

6 Facts and Opinions

School Dinners

Are your school dinners great or rather horrible?
Do you get lots of things that you like?
Do you get too much stodgy stuff like pizza and mashed potato?

Someone in your area is doing a survey of school dinners.
They want you to fill in the form below.
Be fair!
Copy out the form and **fill in** your ideas and opinions.
If you don't take school dinners, invent your answers.

```
Name of school ...................................
I like/don't like my school dinners mainly because
..................................................
I would like less ................................
                  ................................
I would like more ................................
                  ................................

1. Excellent*
2. Good
3. O.K.                    Rating*
4. Not very good          (choose one    ☐
5. Disgusting                number)
```

Your school

Suppose someone asked you if you would recommend your school.
What would you say?
Try to be a fair judge of your school's good and bad points.
Then decide if on balance your school is a good one.

Make a poster for your school.
Write what's best and worst about it.
Be fair!

This is what one nine-year-old wrote about his school.

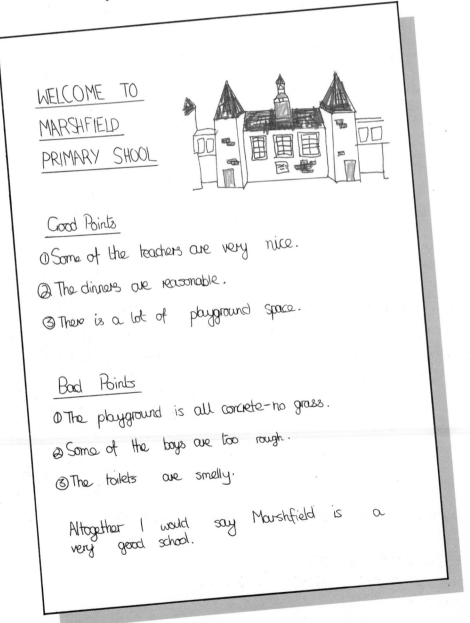

WELCOME TO
MARSHFIELD
PRIMARY SHOOL

Good Points

① Some of the teachers are very nice.

② The dinners are reasonable.

③ There is a lot of playground space.

Bad Points

① The playground is all concrete-no grass.

② Some of the boys are too rough.

③ The toilets are smelly.

Altogether I would say Marshfield is a
very good school.

What do you think?

Write your answers to the puzzles.

1. One morning Angus arrived at school very
    late. His teacher was surprised because
    usually Angus is in the playground
    at 8.50 sharp.

    Why do you think Angus was late for school that day?

    Write: Angus was late because ...

2. Gail is good at spelling. Most Fridays
    she gets 9/10 or 10/10 for her spelling
    test. Today she got only three
    spellings right.

    Why do you think Gail did so badly today?

3. The teacher of Class 6 asked for a
    volunteer to clear out the big cupboard.
    Eddie said he would do it. Usually
    Eddie is not helpful at all!

    Why do you think Eddie volunteered to help the teacher?

Now **write** another puzzle of your own.
Remember there could be lots of different answers
to the question you write.

Look at the statements below.
Discuss them with your friends.
Do you agree or disagree?
Think about your reasons for answering *yes* or *no*.
Write your answer.
Remember to explain **why**.

Schools should be open for only four days a week. *yes/no* WHY?

Everybody should bring a packed lunch to school. *yes/no* WHY?

Girls should do Woodwork the same as boys. *yes/no* WHY?

Popular pets

You are going to make a **Bar Chart** showing which pets
the children in your class have.
First you need to collect your information.
You will need a large sheet of paper ruled out like the one below
(but maybe with different pets).

Cat	Dog	Fish	Hamster	Gerbil	Rabbit	Tortoise	Budgie	None	Total
8	5	2	4	2	1	1	2	3	28

1. First ask everyone about their pet or pets.
   If someone has only a cat, put a tick in the cat box.
   If one person has a fish, a gerbil and a dog,
   put ticks in all three boxes.

2. Add up all the ticks in each of the boxes.

3. Add up the total number of ticks.

4. Make a bar chart showing your results.
   (You can see a Bar Chart in Book 3, page 61.)

5. Decorate your Bar Chart so that other children can see which bar
   represents which pet. You can use different colours for the different
   bars.

Good homes wanted

Every week in the local newspaper there are several ads written by the Cat and Dog Home.
The people who work there collect stray animals and unwanted pets.
They want to find good homes for these cats and dogs.
Here are two recent ads:

Spike and **Milligan** need new friends.
They are three-month-old, black and white collie puppies without a home. They are bouncy, chewy, waggy bundles of fun. Please will someone look after one or both of them?
Please ring the Cat and Dog Home.

Good Home wanted for Fig.
Fig has been abandoned. She is a real softy — a female cat with silky grey fur. She is very gentle. Fig needs someone to love and stroke her.
Please ring Cat and Dog Home.

Write another ad of your own.
Perhaps you would like to write about your own pet.
You want people to take an interest.
Your ad must be persuasive.

A pet for A.P.P.

A.P.P. wants to buy a pet. Help him choose one.
Write a Fact Sheet telling him how to look after his pet.
Divide the information into sections with headings,
so that A.P.P. can understand it.

Like this:

1. Choose an animal or bird that would make a suitable pet for A.P.P.
   (You can write about your own pet if you have one.)

2. Find out all you can about looking after this pet.
   • use library books
   • talk to people who might know (parents, teachers, pet-shop
     owners)
   • use your own ideas

3. Write all the information in rough first.

4. Think of sections and headings for the Fact Sheet.

   Here are some suggestions.
   Think of others if these are not right for **your** Fact Sheet.

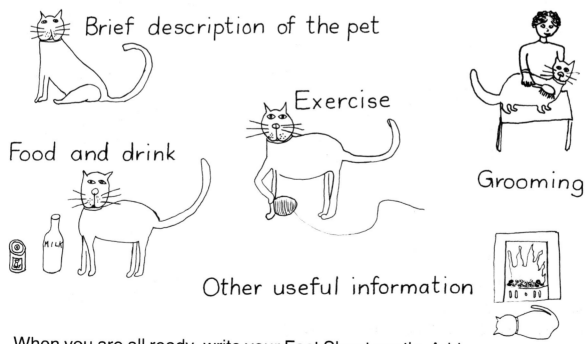

Brief description of the pet

Exercise

Food and drink

Grooming

Other useful information

5. When you are all ready, write your Fact Sheet neatly. Add
   pictures if you want.

Animal Fact Sheet

Jo took part in an exhibition about wildlife in Britain.
His task was to produce a Fact Sheet
about one particular animal or bird.
The Fact Sheet was for young people to look at and read.

1. Jo found out all he could about the grey seal. He looked up information in library books. He watched some seals near the shore.
    He wrote his information in rough first.

2. He chose the most interesting and important facts to include in the Fact Sheet. He did not try to write too much.

3. He arranged the information in sections with headings so that it was easy for young people to read.

Look at the next page to see what he wrote about the grey seal.
Now you choose an animal or bird to find out about.
Write your information in sections with headings.

The Grey Seal

Appearance

The grey seal is a mottled grey - brown, but the colour varies a lot. Baby seals are born with a thick, white, woolly coat which is shed later. Males can grow up to 2.5 metres in length.

Seal Pups

The female comes ashore in early Autumn to give birth to her pups. When the pups are strong enough and have shed their white coats they enter the water and learn how to catch fish.

Habitat

The grey seal is not seen as often as the common seal. There are breeding colonies all along the coast of Scotland and Pembrokeshire and on the Scilly and Lundy Isles. Grey seals like lonely beaches with low rocks and sand and easy access to the water.

Wild life appeal

Imagine you are helping launch an appeal for an animal
that is in danger of dying out.
You can ask people like your teachers about endangered species.
You can look out for information on TV programmes.
You can find out from library books.
You can write to your zoo.
You decide which endangered animal you want to write about.

1. TV Appeal

Write a short piece about your animal to be read
on a children's TV programme.
Here is an example to show what a TV appeal should include.

An introduction

The rhino is now seriously in danger of dying out.

Facts

The rhino is in great danger because large numbers of the animals
are still hunted for their horns. Rhino horns are used
for medicine in the Far East and are thought to have
magical powers. If the hunting continues, there will be
no rhinos left.

An appeal

We need money to help save the rhino. Please send whatever
you can to the World Wild Life Fund here at the studio.

2. Design a Poster

Your Wild Life Appeal poster will appear on buildings and hoardings all over Britain.
It must make adults and children aware of the danger.
It must be eye-catching.
It must persuade people to help by donating money.
Design a poster for the endangered species you have chosen.
Here is one for the rhino.

A.P.P. has come to say goodbye.
He hopes that you have enjoyed working through this book
with him.
He would like to know what you enjoyed about the book.
He would like to know what you have disliked.

Please **list** the three writing tasks you
have most enjoyed. Say why.

Please **list** the three writing tasks you
have least enjoyed. Say why.

Please **fill in** the following short questionnaire.
Copy the chart into your book or onto paper.
Then put a tick in one column for each activity.

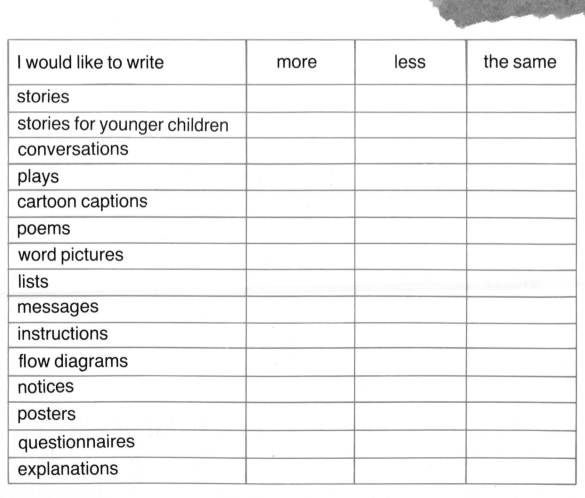

I would like to write	more	less	the same
stories			
stories for younger children			
conversations			
plays			
cartoon captions			
poems			
word pictures			
lists			
messages			
instructions			
flow diagrams			
notices			
posters			
questionnaires			
explanations			